HAN'

Messiah

1741

a sacred oratorio for soprano, alto, tenor & bass soli,
SATB & orchestra

Edited by Ebenezer Prout

NOVELLO
Borough Green   Sevenoaks   Kent

PREFACE

THE present edition of the vocal score of the "Messiah" agrees in its text with the new edition of the full score which I have prepared at the request of the publishers. Of the need of a revised text I have spoken in detail in the preface to the full score, to which readers are referred; it will suffice to say here that the older editions are, without one exception, so inaccurate as to give in many places a most incorrect representation of what Handel really intended.

The text here given is founded upon Handel's autograph—now readily accessible through the photo-lithographed facsimiles—and contemporary transcripts by the composer's amanuensis, Christopher Smith. A collation of these sources has necessitated a very large number of changes in the text both of the vocal and instrumental parts. These are fully noted in the preface to the full score; attention may here be called to a few of the more striking.

In the chorus, "His yoke is easy," Handel's figure—

is incorrectly given—

in all editions nearly every time it occurs. In "Behold the Lamb of God," at bar 16, every edition has in the treble—

In both cases the autograph is perfectly distinct; the mistakes were made at first in the earliest published edition (Randall and Abell's, 1767, though known as Walsh's) of the score, and have been copied without hesitation by all subsequent editors. Similar corrections have been necessary in "Lift up your heads." In bars 27 to 29 Handel writes three times—

which appears incorrectly in all editions, thus—

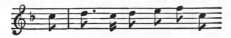

and in the following bars Handel wrote—

The Lord of Hosts

with two quavers (not ♩. ♪) for the word "of."

A still more important mistake occurs in the bass of bars 69 and 70. All editions have—

whereas Handel wrote—

These examples, which are but a few out of many, will suffice to show the need of a revised and purified text.

In his treatment of the words Handel often follows the Italian method, and when one word ends with a vowel and the next word begins with one, he writes only one note for both syllables, e.g., in No. 4—

And the glo - ry, the glo - ry of the Lord.

Just as we can sing " glorious " as a word of two syllables, it is equally easy to sing " glo-ry of " to two notes ; Handel's text is therefore restored here. Similar passages will be found in the " Hallelujah " (alto, bar 24 ; treble, bar 30 ; bass, bars 31 and 32) in each of which the last syllable of the word must be sung to the same note as the first syllable of the same word repeated, thus—

Hal - le - lu - jah, Hal - le - lu - jah,

One more instance of the same procedure will be found in the final chorus, where Handel wrote throughout—

Bless - ing and hon- our, glo-ry and power,

where " -ry and " must be sung as one syllable to the last quaver of the bar, and not to two semiquavers, as given in all earlier editions.

It is well-known to those who have studied the subject that double dots were never, and dotted rests very seldom used in Handel's time, and that consequently the music, if played strictly according to the notation, will in many places not accurately reproduce the composer's intentions. In all such cases I have felt it my duty to give the notes in this edition, not as Handel wrote them, but as he meant them to be played. The full discussion and explanation of these points will be found in the preface to the full score; among the more important examples of this procedure may be instanced the Introduction of the Overture, the recitative, " Thus saith the Lord," and the choruses, " Behold the Lamb of God " and " Surely He hath borne our griefs."

The indications of *piano* and *forte* are for the most part by Handel himself; many of these are wanting in nearly all existing editions. In some cases I have thought it advisable to supplement them, as it is well-known that it was formerly the custom to leave much more to be taught by the conductor at rehearsal than is the case at the present day. For the metronome marks I am responsible; they are not to be necessarily taken as absolutely binding, but only as suggestions of what appears to me to be the suitable *tempo*.

The pianoforte accompaniment is to a great extent new. Of the older arrangements by Dr. Clarke, afterwards Clarke-Whitfeld (1809), and Vincent Novello, but little use could be made, chiefly because they were not so much accompaniments as transcriptions, in which the whole of the voice-parts were included—a method which often necessitated the omission of important features of the orchestration. Besides this, the frequent employment of full chords for the left hand in the lower part of the instrument, common enough in the early part of the last century, is not only contrary to modern usage, but produces a most unpleasant effect.

No attempt has been made to introduce Mozart's contrapuntal additions—*e.g.*, in such movements as " O thou that tellest " or " The people that walked in darkness "—into the accompaniment: first, because it would render it unduly difficult for ordinary use; and secondly, because I have preferred to give Handel's text pure and simple, as far as possible. But I have, of course, filled up the harmony in all cases in which the score contained nothing but a figured bass.

* It is the invariable custom in modern performances to omit a few numbers in the second and third parts of the oratorio. For the sake of completeness these movements are here relegated to an Appendix, in order that the numbers actually performed may follow one another continuously.

London, October, 1902   EBENEZER PROUT

* The numbers formerly included in the appendix have been restored to their original positions, and the paging now agrees with the pocket edition.

December, 1942   NOVELLO AND COMPANY, LIMITED

PART I

PART II

PART III

Nos. 34-36 and 49-52 were formerly printed as an appendix to this edition.—See Preface.

PART I.

OVERTURE.

No. 1.

Handel's Messiah.—Novello's Edition.

8332

4

No. 2. RECITATIVE.—COMFORT YE MY PEOPLE.

cry un-to her, that her war - fare, her war - fare is ac-

-complish'd, that her in - i - qui-ty is par-don'd, that her in-

- i-qui-ty is par - don'd.

The voice of him that cri-eth in the wil-derness, "Pre-pare ye the way of the

Lord, make straight in the des-ert a high-way for our God."

* Handel's MS. has F, the Dublin score D.

No. 5.   RECITATIVE.—THUS SAITH THE LORD.

earth, the sea, the dry land, all na-tions, I'll shake, and the de -

- sire . : . . . . of all

simili.

na - tions shall come.

B *Recit.*

The Lord, whom ye seek, shall sudden-ly come to His

tem-ple, ev'n the messen-ger of the cov-en-ant, whom ye de - light in:

be - hold, He shall come, saith the Lord of Hosts.

No. 6. AIR.—BUT WHO MAY ABIDE THE DAY OF HIS COMING?

com-ing? and who shall stand when He ap - pear-eth?

C

and who shall stand when . . . He ap - pear - -

- - - eth? when . . . He ap - pear - -

D

- eth?

Prestissimo. ♩ = 138.

For He is like . . a re -

8339

ner's fire, for He is like a re-

fi - - - - - - - - - ner's fire,

and who shall stand when He ap - peareth?

F *Larghetto. Tempo 1mo.*

But who may a - bide the day of His com - ing?

and who shall stand, and who shall stand when He ap -

No. 7. CHORUS.—AND HE SHALL PURIFY.

No. 8.   RECITATIVE.—BEHOLD, A VIRGIN SHALL CONCEIVE.

ALTO.

Be - hold,   a   vir - gin shall con - ceive,   and bear a son,

and shall call His name   Em - man - u - el.   "God   with us."

No. 9.   AIR AND CHORUS.—O THOU THAT TELLEST GOOD TIDINGS TO ZION.

Andante. ♪ = 138.

ALTO.

O

O thou that tell-est good ti-dings to Je-ru-sa-lem, lift up thy voice with strength: lift it up, be not a-fraid: say un-to the cit-ies of Ju-dah, say un-to the cit-ies of Ju-dah, Be-hold.. your God! be-hold.. your God! say

un-to the cit-ies of Ju - - dah, Be - hold . . your God! .. be -

- hold your God! . be-hold your God!

O thou that tellest good tidings to Zi-on,

a - rise, shine, for thy light is come,

a rise, a - rise, a - rise, shine, for

8389

CHORUS.

glo - ry of the Lord . . . is ris - en up - on thee.

Lord . . . . . . is ris - en up - on thee.

glo - ry of the Lord . . . is ris - en up - on thee.

glo - ry of the Lord . . . is ris - en up - on thee.

No. 10. RECITATIVE.—FOR BEHOLD, DARKNESS SHALL COVER THE EARTH.

-ry shall be seen up - on thee, and His glo - - - ry shall be seen up-on thee.

And the Gentiles shall come to thy light, and kings to the brightness of thy ri - sing.

No. 11. AIR.—THE PEOPLE THAT WALKED IN DARKNESS.

Larghetto. ♩ = 72.

BASS.

The peo - ple that walk-ed in dark - - ness, that walk-ed in dark -

- ness, the peo - ple that walk - ed, that walk-ed in darkness have

seen a great light; have seen a great light, . . the peo- ple that walk- ed, that

walk - ed in dark-ness have seen a great light, the

B peo- ple that walk- ed, that walk- ed in darkness, that walk-ed in dark - - ness, the

peo- ple that walk-ed in dark - - - ness have seen a great light, have

seen a great light, . . a great light, ... have seen a great light:

mf

C

and they that dwell, . . that

p   *p*

dwell in the land of the shad - - - ow of death, ...

and they that dwell, that dwell in the land, that dwell in the land of the

No. 12.   Chorus.—FOR UNTO US A CHILD IS BORN.

The Mighty God, The Ev-er-last-ing Fa-ther, The Prince of Peace, The

The Mighty God, The Ev-er-last-ing Fa-ther, The Prince of Peace, The

The Mighty God, The Ev-er-last-ing Fa-ther, The Prince of Peace, The

The Mighty God, The Ev-er-last-ing Fa-ther, The Prince of Peace, The

Ev-er-last-ing Fa-ther, The Prince of Peace.

Ev-er-last-ing Fa-ther, The Prince of Peace.

Ev-er-last-ing Fa-ther, The Prince of Peace.

Ev-er-last-ing Father, The Prince of Peace.

No. 18.

PASTORAL SYMPHONY.

8339

No. 14. RECITATIVE.—THERE WERE SHEPHERDS ABIDING IN THE FIELD.

There were shepherds a - biding in the field, keeping watch o - ver their flocks by night.

RECITATIVE.—AND LO, THE ANGEL OF THE LORD CAME UPON THEM.

And lo, the an - gel of the

Lord came up - on them, and the glo - ry of the

Lord shone round a - bout them, and they were sore a - fraid.

No. 15. RECITATIVE.—AND THE ANGEL SAID UNTO THEM.

No. 16. RECITATIVE.—AND SUDDENLY THERE WAS WITH THE ANGEL.

No. 17.

CHORUS.—GLORY TO GOD.

No. 18.   AIR.—REJOICE GREATLY, O DAUGHTER OF ZION!

Handel's MS. reads—

be - hold, thy King cometh un - to . . thee,

un - to thee!

f

He is the right - - eous

p *tr* *f* *p*

Sa - viour, and He shall speak peace un-to the hea -

poco cres. *p*

- then, He shall speak peace, He shall speak peace, peace, He shall speak

peace un-to the hea - - then, He is . . the right - - eous Sa - viour, and He shall speak, He shall speak peace, peace, . . . He shall speak peace . . un-to the hea - - then. Re-joice, re-joice, re - joice . . . greatly, re - joice . . . . . .

shout, re - joice . . . great-ly,

re-joice . . greatly, O daughter of Zi - on! Shout, . .

. . O daugh-ter of Je - ru - sa-lem! Be-hold, thy King cometh un - to

thee! be - hold thy King com-eth un - to thee!

No. 19. RECITATIVE.—THEN SHALL THE EYES OF THE BLIND BE OPENED.

No. 20. AIR.—HE SHALL FEED HIS FLOCK LIKE A SHEPHERD.

Come un-to .. Him, .. all ye that la - bour, come un - to .. Him, ye that are .. hea-vy la - den, and He will give you rest, come un - to .. Him, .. all ye that la - bour, come un - to .. Him, ye that are hea-vy la - den, and He will give you rest.

Take His yoke up-on you, and learn .. of Him, . for

No. 21.   Chorus.—HIS YOKE IS EASY, AND HIS BURTHEN IS LIGHT.

PART II.

No. 22.

CHORUS.—BEHOLD THE LAMB OF GOD.

No. 23.

AIR.—HE WAS DESPISED.

them that pluck-ed off the hair, and his cheeks to them that pluck-ed off the

F

hair: He hid not His face from shame and

spit-ting, He hid not His face from shame, . .

from shame, . . . He hid not His

face from shame, ... from shame and spit-ting.

D.C.

p

No. 24. CHORUS.—SURELY HE HATH BORNE OUR GRIEFS.

Segue No. 25.

No. 25. CHORUS.—AND WITH HIS STRIPES WE ARE HEALED.

8332

Segue No. 26.
6332

No. 26.   CHORUS.—ALL WE LIKE SHEEP HAVE GONE ASTRAY.

No. 27.   RECITATIVE.—ALL THEY THAT SEE HIM, LAUGH HIM TO SCORN.

8339

No. 30.   AIR.—BEHOLD, AND SEE IF THERE BE ANY SORROW.

No. 81. Recitative.—HE WAS CUT OFF OUT OF THE LAND OF THE LIVING.

No. 32. Air.—BUT THOU DIDST NOT LEAVE HIS SOUL IN HELL.

soul in .. hell, nor didst .. Thou suf-fer, nor didst Thou suf - fer Thy

Ho - ly .. One to see cor-rup - tion.

But Thou didst not leave His

soul in hell, Thou didst not leave, Thou didst not leave His

soul in hell, nor didst Thou suf - fer Thy

No. 38.   CHORUS.—LIFT UP YOUR HEADS, O YE GATES.

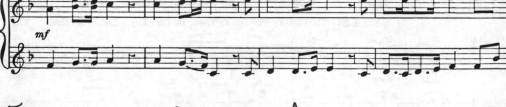

* Handel's MS. has "this King," not "the King."

- ry,

Glo - - - ry, of Glo - ry, the Lord of Hosts, He is the King..

Glo - - ry, the Lord of Hosts, He

the Lord of Hosts, He

the Lord of Hosts, He is the King of Glo - - - - -

...of Glo - - ry, of Glo - - - - -

is the King of Glo - ry, of Glo - - - ry, of Glo - -

is the King of Glo - ry, of Glo - -

- - ry, He is the King of Glo-ry, He is the King of Glo-ry, the Lord of Hosts,

- - ry, He is the King of Glo-ry, He is the King of Glo-ry, the Lord of

- - ry, He is the King of Glo-ry, He is the King of Glo-ry, the Lord of

- - ry, He is the King of Glo-ry, He is the King of Glo-ry, the Lord of

No. 84. RECITATIVE.—**UNTO WHICH OF THE ANGELS SAID HE AT ANY TIME.**

No. 85. CHORUS.—**LET ALL THE ANGELS OF GOD WORSHIP HIM.**

125

No. 36.

AIR.—THOU ART GONE UP ON HIGH.

Thou art gone up on high, Thou art gone up on high,

Thou hast led cap-tiv - i - ty cap - tive, Thou hast led cap-tiv - i - ty

cap - tive, and re - ceiv - - - - - ed gifts . . for men; yea,

might dwell a-mong them.

Thou art gone up on high, Thou art gone up on high, Thou hast

led cap-tiv - i - ty cap - tive, Thou hast led cap-tiv - i - ty cap - tive,

and re - ceiv - ed gifts for men; yea, e - ven

for Thine en - - - - - - - -

God might dwell a - mong them, might dwell . . . .

100

a - mong .

them, that the Lord God might dwell a - mong them.

110

190

No. 87.   Chorus.—THE LORD GAVE THE WORD.

great was the com-pa-ny of the preachers, of the preachers, great was the com

pa-ny, the com pa-ny, the com pa-ny, the

great was the com-pa-ny of the preachers, the com pa-ny, the

pa-ny, the com pa-ny, the com

pa - - - ny of the preach - ers, of the preach -

com - pa - ny, the com pa-ny, the com-pa-ny of the preach - ers, of the preach -

com - - ny, tho com - ny of the preach - ers, of the preach -

pa-ny, the com pa-ny of the preach - ers, of the preach -

ers.

ers.

ers.

ers.

No. 38. **AIR.—HOW BEAUTIFUL ARE THE FEET.**

Larghetto. ♪ = 104.

Soprano.

How beau-ti-ful are the feet of them that

preach the gos-pel of peace, how beau-ti-ful are the feet, how

beau-ti-ful are the feet of them that preach the gos-pel of peace,

A

how beau-ti-ful are the feet.. of them that

8332

No. 89. **CHORUS.—THEIR SOUND IS GONE OUT INTO ALL LANDS.**

No. 40. AIR.—WHY DO THE NATIONS SO FURIOUSLY RAGE TOGETHER.

do the peo-ple im-ag-ine a vain thing? why

do the na-tions rage . . . .

. . . . . . so fu-rious-ly to-

-ge-ther? why do the peo-ple im-

-ag - - - - - ine a . . vain

thing? . . . . im-ag - - - ine a vain

thing? why do the

na - tions so fu-rious-ly rage to-ge-ther, and

why do the peo-ple, and why do the

peo-ple im-ag - ine a . . vain thing? . . why

do the na - tions rage . . . .

. . . . so fu - rious-ly to -

- ge - ther, so fu-rious-ly to - ge - ther? and why do the

peo - ple im - ag - ine a vain thing? im -

- ag - - - - ine a vain thing? and

why do the peo-ple im-ag-ine a vain

thing?

The

kings of the earth rise up, and the ru-lers take coun-sel to-

-ge-ther, take coun

sel, take coun - - sel to - - ge - ther against the Lord, and a - gainst . . . His a - - noint - - - - - - - - - ed, a-gainst the Lord, and His a - noint - - - - - - - - - ed.

Segue Chorus, No. 41.

No. 41. CHORUS.—LET US BREAK THEIR BONDS ASUNDER

- way their yokes from us, let us break their bonds, and cast a -

- way their yokes, . . let us break their bonds, their bonds a - sun - der, and cast a -

- way their yokes, let us break their bonds a - sun - der, their bonds a - sun - der, and cast a -

- way their yokes from us, let us break their bonds a - sun - der, and cast a -

- way, and cast a - way their yokes from us.

- way, and cast a - way their yokes from us.

- way, and cast a - way their yokes from us.

- way, and cast a - way their yokes from us.

No. 42.   RECITATIVE.—HE THAT DWELLETH IN HEAVEN.

He that dwelleth in heaven shall laugh them to scorn; the Lord shall have them in de-ri-sion.

No. 43.   AIR.—THOU SHALT BREAK THEM.

Andante. ♩ = 84.

Thou shalt break them,   Thou shalt break them with a rod .... of i - ron;

poco cres.

Chorus.—HALLELUJAH!

Handel's Messiah.—Novello's Edition.

* See Preface.

8332

PART III.

No. 45.   Air.—I KNOW THAT MY REDEEMER LIVETH.

8339

day . . . . . . up - on the earth,

B

I know that my Re - deem - er liv - eth, and that

He shall stand . . . . . . at the lat - ter day up - on the

C

earth, ... up - on the earth, I know . . . that my Re -

- deem - er liv - eth, and He shall stand . . . . at the lat - - - ter day

know that my Re - deem - er liv - eth. And though worms de - stroy this

bo - dy, yet in my flesh shall I see God, yet in my

flesh . . . shall I see God, shall I see God. I know that my Re -

- - deem - er liv-eth. For now is Christ ris - en

from the dead, the first - - fruits of them that

No. 46.   CHORUS.—SINCE BY MAN CAME DEATH.

raised in - cor - rup-ti - ble, and we shall be changed, . . .

and

we shall be changed.

Trumpet. The

trum-pet shall sound, . . . the trum -pet shall sound, . . .

* This second part of the Air is generally omitted.

mor - tal must put . . on im-mor - tal

- - i - ty, and this mor - tal must put on im - mor - tal -

- - - - i - ty, im - mor - tal - i - ty. The

Dal X

No. 49. RECITATIVE.—THEN SHALL BE BROUGHT TO PASS.

No. 50. DUET.—O DEATH, WHERE IS THY STING?

N.B.—This Duet is given in the abridged form indicated by Handel in the Dublin score. Compare the Full Score.

No. 51.   Chorus.—BUT THANKS BE TO GOD.

God,
Who giv-eth us the vic-to-ry, the

Who giv-eth us the vic - to-ry,
Who giv-eth us the

God,
Who giv-eth us the vic - to-ry,
Who giv-eth us the

Who giv-eth us the

vic - to-ry through our Lord Je - sus Christ, but thanks be to God, but thanks,

vic - to-ry through our Lord Je - sus Christ, but thanks, thanks be to God, but

vic - to-ry through our Lord Je - sus Christ, but thanks be to God, but

vic - to-ry through our Lord Je - sus Christ, but thanks be to God, but

but thanks, thanks be to God, to God, Who giv-eth us the

thanks, but thanks, thanks be to God,

thanks, but thanks, thanks be to God, Who

thanks, but thanks, thanks . . . be to God, Who

No. 52. AIR.—IF GOD BE FOR US, WHO CAN BE AGAINST US?

who is he that con - demn-eth? who is he that com - demn - - - - - - eth?

It is Christ that di - ed, yea ra - ther, that is ris - en a - gain,

Who is at the right hand of God, Who

right hand of God, Who is at the right hand of God, at the right hand of God,

Who makes in - ter - ces - sion for us.

Adagio.

ad lib.

f a tempo.

160

tr

tr

tr

tr

tr

tr

170

No. 53.   CHORUS.—WORTHY IS THE LAMB THAT WAS SLAIN.

sitteth upon the throne, that sitteth upon the throne, . . for ev - er and ev . . -

that sitteth upon the throne for ev - er and ev -

Blessing and honour, glory and pow'r, be un - to

. . . . . . and un - to the Lamb for ev - er and ev - -

- er, and un - to the Lamb for . .

- er, and un - to the Lamb for . . .

Him. Bless - ing and hon - our, glo - ry and pow'r, be un - to Him for

- er. Bless - ing and hon - our, glo - ry and pow'r, be un - to Him for

50

ev - - er. Bless - ing and hon - our, glo - ry and pow'r, be un - to

ev - er. Bless - ing and hon - our, glo - ry and pow'r, be un - to

ev - - er. Bless - ing and hon - our, glo - ry and pow'r, be un - to

ev - - er.

Handel's Messiah.—Novello's Edition.

8332

THE END

Choral Music
OF THE 16th & 17th CENTURIES

Giovanni Gabrieli

IN ECCLESIIS
motet for soloists, chorus, strings, instruments & organ.
Edited by Denis Stevens

Claudio Monteverdi

BEATUS VIR
for SSATTB chorus, instruments & organ. Edited by John Steele

MAGNIFICAT
for soloists, double choir, organ & orchestra.
Edited by John Steele & Denis Stevens

VESPERS
for soloists, double choir, organ & orchestra.
Edited by Denis Stevens

Giovanni da Palestrina

MISSA PAPAE MARCELLI
for unaccompanied SSATBB chorus. Edited by Otto Goldschmidt

STABAT MATER
motet for unaccompanied double choir. Edited by W. Barclay Squire

---

Giovanni Rovetta

LAUDATE DOMINUM
for SS(A)A(T)TB chorus, instruments & organ. Edited by John Steele

---

Alessandro Scarlatti

AUDI FILIA
for SSA solo, SSATB chorus, instruments, string orchestra & organ.
Edited by John Steele

ST. CECILIA MASS (1720)
for SSATB soli & chorus, string orchestra & organ.
Edited by John Steele

Heinrich Schütz

THE PASSION
a selection from the 'Four Passions'. ATB soli, chorus & organ

novello